# Endorsements

Amy speaks from both experience and expertise, and this book is a beautiful culmination of this. Using the natural elements to help you connect with the grief cycle, which often follows a late ADHD diagnosis, is both novel and insightful. As a woman who received an ADHD diagnosis in adulthood, I recommend newly diagnosed people to read this book. It prompts you to reflect, reconnect, and embrace and celebrate your new sense of self, post diagnosis.

**Roxanne Rogers, Postgraduate Qualitative Researcher and Woman with ADHD**

Amy's skilled and compassionate questions create a powerful self-guided journal to untangle your emotions, process your journey, and allow you to experience a gradual unfolding into your own acceptance, change, growth, and empowerment. *Unique Minds* provides a steadfast and loving guide to process your late ADHD diagnosis. Amy poetically invites you to embrace your new identity, shift your roadblocks into steppingstones, and discover the power that comes with that. She courageously shares her own intimate stories of shock, internal emotional weather, and vulnerability as she untangled and navigated her own journey to acceptance and wisdom. This beautiful journal will guide you to your own place of acceptance and wisdom.

**Jean Sheridan, Wellbeing Coach**

Immediately I felt connected to Amy with our shared experiences in my ADHD diagnosis. There have been many instances in my journey where I felt alone and that others could not relate. This journal broke down those insecurities I've struggled with and shone a light of hope and gratitude that I didn't even know I needed. Each question she poses brought insightful thoughts that hadn't crossed my mind in the past year. Finding the joy in the journey, looking at myself with kindness, and seeing the beauty in my unique mind was exactly what I needed.

**Sadie Tollberg, BSN, RN and Army Veteran Health Coach**

The strength of this journal lies in its ability to address the multifaceted emotional journey that individuals embark upon when confronting ADHD. With compassion, Amy explores the initial shock, the stages of grief, and the ultimate triumphs that emerge when embracing neurodiversity.

**Tamara Rosier, Ph.D. Author: *Your Brain's Not Broken***

Amy flawlessly aligns the five stages of grief with the five elements to assist women newly diagnosed with ADHD. Her practical journaling techniques effectively manage the complexities of an ADHD diagnosis. This book offers valuable insights from a compassionate and personal standpoint, making it beneficial for anyone facing an ADHD diagnosis.

**Rebekah Reineke, Woman with ADHD**

When Amy Joynt writes, "Self-discovery is the most freeing thing you can do in a world that often wants you to fit in", I raised my cheerleading pom poms to the sky, because she hits the nail on its proverbial head. As an ADHDer and ADHD coach, Amy's experiences echo my own and those of many other late-diagnosed humans. A late diagnosis of ADHD can leave you feeling lost and bewildered, and life often doesn't make space for you to process your emotions and readjust your world view. There's no handbook or sat-nav for this process. This is why *Unique Minds* is a much-needed resource for ADHDers following a formal or self-diagnosis. As well as speaking candidly about her own experiences, Amy accompanies you through a journey of realization and reflection. Using carefully crafted reflection questions, *Unique Minds* helps you to look compassionately at past, present and future you, your unique brain, and your strengths and talents. Buy it, read it, and carry it with you as you walk your life post-diagnosis.

**Anj Caims, ADHD Coach**

Self-guided journals following a new diagnosis, for me, would be helpful because I sometimes don't know where to start. Knowing that there is someone out there who has gone through something akin to what I am experiencing means I am not alone, and when that person has created such a well-crafted guide to help navigate some of the questions, it alleviates much of the anxiety that is associated with the experience. Having an effective guide is important to the process when you can't just exercise more or meditate or speak with a friend. Knowing that someone else to whom I can relate has not only made it through all the stages but will be there to hold my hand through my journey, is powerful.

**Ken Holt, Diagnosed with ADHD and PTSD**

# UNIQUE MINDS

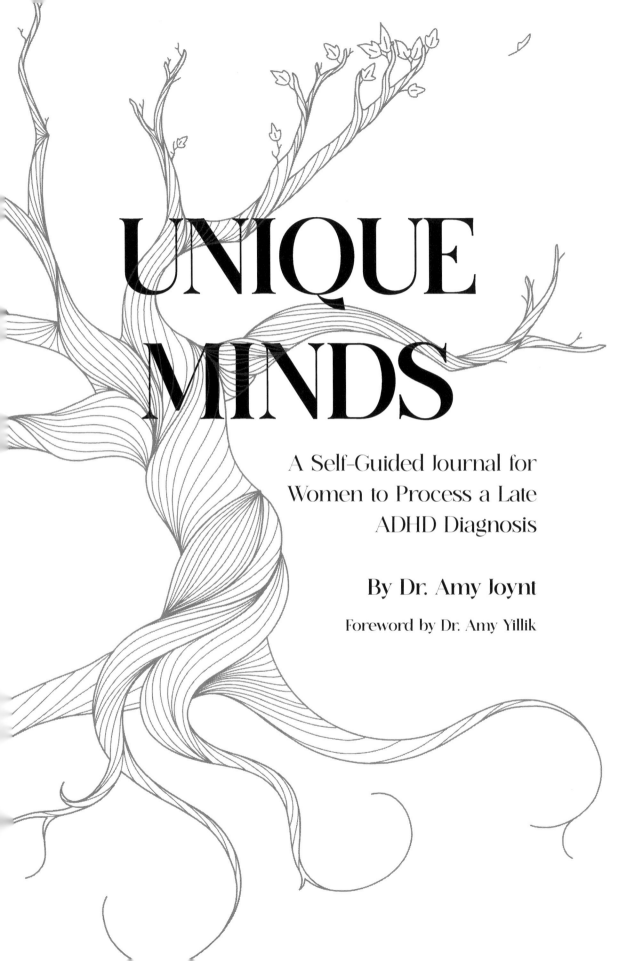

# UNIQUE MINDS

## A Self-Guided Journal for Women to Process a Late ADHD Diagnosis

### By Dr. Amy Joynt

Foreword by Dr. Amy Yillik

Unique Minds: A Self-Guided Journal for Women to Process a Late ADHD Diagnosis

© 2024 by Dr. Amy Joynt

First printing 2024

LIBRARY OF CONGRESS CATALOGING

Cataloging-in-Publication data available

Library of Congress Control Number: 2024900148

ISBN 979-8-9897937-0-9 (international trade paperback)

ISBN 979-8-9897937-1-6 (e-book)

Cover & Interior Design: Holly Dunn hollydunndesign.com

Editor: Celina Mina createwithcelina.com

Illustrator: Jaima Zollinger

Author Photo: Kevin Joynt

*Keep some room in your heart for the unimaginable*

Mary Oliver[1]

# CONTENTS

# FOREWORD

## by Dr. Amy Yillik

D r. Amy Joynt's initial disbelief in being diagnosed with attention deficit hyperactivity disorder (ADHD) as an adult is relatable. As someone who has been diagnosing the neurological disorder for almost three decades, I have experienced feelings of denial as women in my life began to receive these diagnoses in adulthood during the past few years. As their friend who happens to be a practitioner, I found myself thinking I must be a sham of a psychologist that I couldn't see their struggles as symptoms of ADHD. The truth is the field of diagnosing ADHD was initially myopic. So much of our knowledge about ADHD stemmed from ADHD in males and how their symptoms often present. Males are more likely to exhibit hyperactivity, impulsivity, and aggression, while females generally demonstrate forgetfulness, disorganization, and distractibility.[2] It is easy to see how we have overlooked or even dismissed female ADHD symptoms when the male expression of ADHD is often louder and demands immediate attention.

Amy and I have known each other for over a decade—first as colleagues, now as friends. Her raw and vulnerable discussion of her own adult diagnosis of ADHD shines a light on a path of hope for other women who are also struggling to navigate recent diagnoses. Research on women that have been diagnosed with ADHD in adulthood highlights the extreme challenges of growing up without appropriate support and intervention. Undiagnosed females often grow up believing themselves to be *dumb*, *lazy*, or overly-

*dramatic*, and can go on to have a myriad of secondary issues from mental illness to addiction.[3] In *Unique Minds*, Dr. Joynt walks alongside the reader on this personal journey, sharing her experiences and helping to shift the false narrative that many women believe. Her bravery in telling her story gives the reader permission to also be brave and unlearn the untruths to reveal the unique assets neurodivergent women possess. I have no doubt that this workbook will help women to navigate their new diagnosis to uncover something that may have once been a point of shame—seeing themselves not as broken nor bad, but instead as creative, spontaneous, hyper-focused, skilled in communication, energetic, courageous, and resilient—as their superpowers! I can't help but believe that my friend Dr. Amy Joynt will soon feel like your friend as well as you travel on your journey of discovery through *Unique Minds: A Self-Guided Journal for Women to Process a Late ADHD Diagnosis*.

*Dr. Amy Yillik has worked in the field of education since the 1990s. She is a licensed school counselor and psychologist, an educational consultant with Culture of Care in Oregon, and adjunct faculty in USC Rossier's School of Education School Counseling program.*

# INTRODUCTION

## Diagnosis, Aftermath, and Navigating Your Neurodivergent Journey

I was given a life-changing diagnosis at the age of thirty-nine. ADHD. This revelation was a perplexing mix of comfort and shock. For the first time, the scattered puzzle pieces of my existence connected, and I saw the greater picture. This newfound awareness, however, was followed by a whirlwind of emotions. I struggled with the idea that I had expended so much energy concealing my troubles and bearing the weight of the world on my shoulders—all at the expense of my mental and emotional health.

**Take a deep breath.**

Consider whether this experience resonates with you.

Time seemed to stand still when I was diagnosed with ADHD.

I glanced back into the mirror of my history, but the image was no longer familiar. I could see myself as the little girl I used to be, frequently ordered to shut up or to stop being so emotional. There was a pause in time, laced with uncertainty and worry for what was ahead.

With the benefit of hindsight, I can see the importance of that suspended moment. It wasn't just the medical prescription or the title I was given; it was the birth of a new perspective. A chance to rewind the tape of my life and embark upon a voyage of reconnection—with the person I was, the person I was becoming, and the unique individual I was always supposed to be.

**Take another deep breath.**

**How does this relate to your own experience?**

All journeys, whether physical or intellectual, are full of surprises and unexpected landscapes. Imagine navigating an unknown forest with nothing but your wits and the wilderness for companionship. This frightening image may possibly reflect the confusion that many people experience when they receive a new diagnosis. This perfectly describes my experience.

I struggled with emotions of shame for failing to fit into society's expectations.

I struggled with feelings of inadequacy, an erroneous fear that I wasn't putting in enough effort.

I felt alone.

This captures the wild journey that many neurodivergent people begin after obtaining a diagnosis—a plunge into an intricate depth of emotions and a flurry of thoughts.

This process can feel lonely and intimidating.

Your journey, following a diagnosis, does not have to be solitary. *Unique Minds* is your steadfast guide, your trusted partner, and your light in the darkness.

In a culture that persistently demands that we hide our troubles and trade the real for the ideal, it takes exceptional courage to remove the façade and openly accept and express our vulnerabilities. I'm inviting you to join me on a journey of self-discovery, growth, and liberation shaped by a late diagnosis.

This diagnosis did more than just clarify my past; it exposed my current challenges and provided me with the language to express them. More importantly, it functioned as a compass, directing me to a clearer understanding of my qualities and potential. This shaped my vision for a greater future. I believe that through our shared experiences, we can find peace, understanding, and the healing power of collective strength.

Years after my diagnosis, I realized I hadn't given myself the pause I needed to process my diagnosis.

I hadn't stopped to use that time as an opportunity for self-discovery.

I had carried on—business as usual.

That was a mistake.

I was denying myself of the chance to heal.

However, when I was jolted by an unexpected change in life circumstances, I was forced to pause. Instead of continuing to fight against myself, I chose to look to nature's elements for guidance. I chose to process my diagnosis.

*I discovered resilience in the embrace of the elements, a reminder that I, too, am woven into the fabric of the natural world, intimately attached to the rhythm and bound to its cycles.*

Self-discovery is the most freeing thing you can do in a world that often wants you to fit in. It begins with the acceptance of a deep truth:

You are not a square peg trying to fit into a round hole; you are one-of-a-kind, built with curves and angles that tell an astonishing tale.

Your neurodivergent journey is not about becoming 'normal'. It's about understanding, accepting, and appreciating your mind's genuine uniqueness.

*Unique Minds* begins with the ferocious intensity of denial. We tumble into the chaotic cascades of anger and sadness, purifying like a waterfall. We're propelled forward by the unpredictability of bargaining until we discover tranquility in the cradle of acceptance—as firm and reassuring as the earth underneath us. Our voyage concludes with the vastness and freedom we gain from self-love.

When we move forward into the light, we no longer see our flaws as burdens. They become symbols of our common human experience. We provide a platform for true self-expression. As your guide on this journey, I come from a place of understanding. I have seen how powerful it can be to use a diagnosis like ADHD as a steppingstone instead of a roadblock to self-awareness.

*Unique Minds: A Self-Guided Journal for Women to Process a Late ADHD Diagnosis* is an intimate chronicle of my journey and the wisdom I've unearthed along the way. It is a light of hope for those who, like me, have struggled with the heavy weight of a late diagnosis and the enormous emotional burden that comes with it.

Will you join me on this journey?

# HOW TO USE THIS JOURNAL

This journal guides you through the emotional landscapes encountered while processing a mental health diagnosis. It navigates the stages of grief, viewing them through the symbolic lens of nature's elements. Each element represents a distinct stage of grief, providing unique insights and perspectives on this transformative journey.

*But remember—grief has no rules.*

We must be compassionate with ourselves as we ride the emotional roller coaster of a new diagnosis.

There is no correct or incorrect way to feel.

No feeling is forbidden.

We can achieve peace and acceptance by submitting to these feelings and processing them in a healthy way. If you find yourself experiencing feelings of anger, sadness, or any other emotions while working through this journal, know that you are not alone.

Give yourself permission to process your grief in your own time, in your own way.

This journal is organized in a linear manner, following the well-established phases of grief. However, **it's crucial to note that the route to healing, especially for neurodivergent people, rarely follows a straight line.**

Don't be surprised if you're pulled to the crashing waves of despair and fury before the smoldering embers of denial, or if you sense the call of the grounded soil before the releasing breezes of bargaining.

Not only is this understandable, but it exemplifies the special cadence of our neurodivergent thinking.

I encourage you to acknowledge and accept the wisdom of this rhythm, to listen to your inner guidance, and to engage with this journal in the way that best suits your unique journey.

Allow your intuition to lead you through the pages; there is no 'right' path in this self-discovery. The path is yours.

The goal of this journal is to help you embrace your identity as a neurodivergent individual, to equip you with the tools needed to navigate your unique path, and to discover the power that comes from acceptance and self-love.

**There are a variety of exercises and activities designed to assist you in untangling the intricate web of your emotions, identifying your strengths and challenges, and building a framework to manage the ebbs and flows of the neurodivergent experience.** These tools are not only intended to aid knowledge, but also to empower you on your journey of self-discovery.

Within these pages, we will delve into the frequently misunderstood concept of neurodivergent masking—the layers we wear to conform to society's standards. By peeling back these layers, we establish techniques to reduce the need for masking, allowing us to celebrate our unique qualities as the strengths they truly are.

Each chapter ends with a **Moving Forward** section, which concentrates on healing, growth, and empowerment using specific exercises. It inspires you to embrace your neurodivergent individuality, ignite your inner flame, and thrive in a world that may appear overwhelming.

So, let us go on this journey together, standing tall in the middle of life's ups and downs, our real selves beaming light toward the way ahead.

Let us not consider this a race; it is a gradual unfolding—a blossoming of a unique and lovely individual.

You.

Let us explore the depths of our emotions together.

Let us seek acceptance, healing, and, ultimately, liberation.

# PART 1

## Fire—Denial

*I am holding both my hope and grief together in the same hands.*
*Tallu Schuyler Quinn[4]*

My diagnosis served as a catalyst, requiring a renegotiation between my newly revealed reality and long-held ideas about myself. I was faced with a great internal conflict, a silent war raging within the depths of my consciousness.

I repeatedly found myself in the grip of self-blame, viewing my difficulties as flaws and failures rather than as signs of a misunderstood condition. A persistent voice within me asserted that I only needed to push harder and that the mess in my life was the product of laziness or a lack of will. The more I tried to fit into the traditional mold, the fiercer the internal conflict became. This internal conflict was, in fact, a powerful type of denial—a stubborn resistance to embrace the reality of my unique neurological design.

Take a small break for introspection.

Is any of this like your own experience?

This denial was more than a spark; it was an all-consuming inferno that devoured every facet of my identity. It raged against my self-concept, destroying everything I believed I knew about myself. All the explanations I'd crafted—the stories I'd built around my perceived shortcomings to feel 'normal'—were trapped in this raging blaze.

In its relentless sweep, the fire of denial reduced my history to ashes, changing what was once familiar into an unfamiliar world of dust and broken recollections.

I stood among the ruins of my former life, struck by the sharp knowledge that my inner self had been hidden beneath a façade that was out of sync with the person I truly was.

**I have come to realize that despite the pain, I discovered a fundamental truth.**

Like the mythological phoenix rising from the ashes, the wreckage of denial may cultivate the seeds of an empowered new understanding.

A new perspective could be cobbled together from the shattered pieces of the old one, recognizing and celebrating the unique aspects of a neurodivergent brain. **This was the first tumultuous step toward learning to love my brain's rhythm rather than working against it.**

In retrospect, I see the wildfire as an important part of my—and your—journey.

It shattered my misconceptions, paving the way for newfound growth and a **deeper soil of understanding** in which to plant a seed that would later blossom into my real self.

You, too, can discover restoration and regeneration in the ashes of denial just as a forest can after a wildfire.

I imagine that as we go through these fiery landscapes together, we will find strength, understanding, and acceptance among the ashes of what once was.

Facing the flames involves examining terrain that will appear both scary and unknown. We are on the edge of falling into denial, a powerful force capable of erecting barriers between our perspective and reality.

Denial has the ferocity of a firestorm, both destructive and purifying. In this part, we will explore the complexities of how denial shows up in our diagnosis.

I'd like to take you on a tour down memory lane, reviewing those spark-filled occasions that ignited the firestorm of denial. Expect a revival of disbelief; you may challenge the veracity of the diagnosis or reject it as an error. While these recollections may elicit strong emotions, keep in mind that they, like fire, have the capacity to illuminate our path forward.

We will uncover the function that medication or other therapeutic interventions can have in this part of the journey. Please bear in mind that while medication is discussed in this journal, it is not suitable for everyone. This journal is for both people taking medication and those who are not. I felt compelled to include medication in this journal for two reasons. One being that it is frequently recommended accompanying a new diagnosis.

Sometimes, that is the only recommendation.

Second, medication is often required to manage neurodivergence. Accepting the fact that medication is a requisite can be a symbol of acceptance. On the other hand, it can be an unintentional fuel for denial. **That isn't to argue that people who choose to be unmedicated aren't accepting of their condition.** For me, medication was used to manipulate my diagnosis in an unhelpful way. We will examine these points of view to gain a balanced picture of the function that medication can serve in our lives.

This part emphasizes the significance of reaching out, revealing the lifelines of support that can draw us toward understanding and acceptance. Recognizing that a diagnosis can open the way for growth is critical. It helps to reframe our perspective, realizing both the difficulties and the opportunity that a diagnosis can bring.

**By the end of this part, I hope you'll have a better grasp of denial, its function in our grief process, and how it can act as a catalyst propelling us toward greater self-love.**

This step, albeit painful, is an essential part of our journey.

Peel back the layers of denial to reveal the way to understanding. Your journey through the first stage of grief begins right here.

# Moving Forward

Remember, there's no right or wrong answer here.

As with any fire, treat this process with respect and caution.

Don't be afraid to seek support if the heat becomes too intense.

Let the memories unfold, paying attention to its nuances, and observe the impressions it has left in your psyche.

*Think about the time leading up to your diagnosis.*

Create a timeline of events, experiences, or symptoms that you noticed prior to seeking a diagnosis.

What 'red flags' did you have about yourself that led to seeking a diagnosis?

--------------------------------------------------------------------

--------------------------------------------------------------------

--------------------------------------------------------------------

--------------------------------------------------------------------

*Remember your diagnosis.*

Close your eyes and allow yourself to be transported back in time to the moment your diagnosis became known for the first time.

Consider the scene in detail: the room, the people in it, the words spoken and written, the smells, the season, and anything else that describes this memory.

Describe the scene here:

--------------------------------------------------------------------

--------------------------------------------------------------------

_____

_____

_____

_____

_____

Upon hearing the news, were you knocked off your feet by a wildfire of disbelief or did it gradually smolder?

Try to remember the emotions you felt at the time and record them here.

Where in your body did you feel these emotions?

_____

_____

_____

_____

_____

_____

*Confront denial.*

In what ways did denial manifest itself in your behavior or your thoughts?

For me, as mentioned previously, I initially kept moving forward with my life for a long time as if nothing changed.

I didn't begin to process the denial I felt until much later.

This may also be true for you.

_____

_____

_____

_____

_____

Can you identify any protective factors that denial provided for you?

How might it have been trying to shield you from discomfort or pain?

For example, did you hide your diagnosis from others?

Did you double down on masking?

Did you tell yourself that the person who diagnosed you made a mistake? If so, how?

Did you minimize the diagnosis? And if so, in what way?

Did you tell yourself that it wasn't a diagnosis but rather a personality flaw?

_____

_____

_____

_____

_____

_____

Pause and reflect on any stigmas associated with your diagnosis.

Jot down any myths of misconceptions you've encountered or believed.

Beside each, note the factual information you've discovered to dispel these misunderstandings.

_____

_____

_____

_____

_____

Have you ever felt judged or stigmatized because of the symptoms or behaviors related to your condition before you had a name for it?

Describe those instances.

_____

_____

_____

_____

_____

With a clearer understanding of your diagnosis, consider how you can transform misconceptions and stigmas into empowering self-talk that celebrates neurodiversity.

Use the space below to reframe any self-doubting beliefs into positive, neurodiverse affirming language.

_____

_____

_____

_____

_____

_____

*View medication as a firefighting tool.*

If your treatment included medication, I invite you to take a moment to reflect on this aspect of your journey.

*Remember, this journal is not intended to judge anyone for using or not using medication.* How did you initially respond to the idea of medication?

Did you see it as a potential elixir that could ease your symptoms or did the process feel more like a challenging quest to find the right balance?

_____

_____

_____

_____

Did you explore other strategies alongside medication to manage your diagnosis?

    If so, what were they?

    How did they make you feel?

_____

_____

_____

_____

_____

As you navigated this new path, did the process of trial and error with medication and other strategies make you feel more in control, or did it leave you feeling helpless at times?

_____

_____

_____

_____

_____

_____

Reflect on the steps you've taken to reclaim control over your life post-diagnosis.

What moments gave you a sense of empowerment or progress?

_____

_____

_____

_____

_____

*Walk through the blaze.*

As you reflect on the path you've traveled since your diagnosis, pay close attention to the emotions that resurface and where they show up in the body.

Are you still engulfed by the flames or are the beginnings of acceptance starting to form amid the smoke?

This space provides an opportunity to assess your progress and contemplate your next steps toward continued healing and self-discovery.

_____

_____

_____

_____

_____

*Prepare to travel past denial.*

Take a deep breath in and visualize the flames fading, revealing a road to acceptance and self-discovery.

Feel a spark of bravery and vulnerability kindle within you, inspiring you to recognize and accept your distinct neurodivergence.

Consider yourself standing on the rim of a dormant volcano, surrounded by a desolate environment.

The scarcely visible embers beneath your feet mirror your boiling denial.

Recognize the denial that is keeping you from truly embracing your neurodivergent identity.

What worries or uncertainties are preventing you from accepting your diagnosis?

What do you need to let go of in order to move past this stage?

Imagine the embers cooling and morphing into a solid foundation.

Feel the earth beneath you harden, allowing you to rise from the ashes of denial with strength and tenacity, embracing your neurodivergent identity.

Use the space below to capture any words or images that are still lingering.

Part 1 dealt with the first stage of grief—denial.

We gave space to fully experience our emotions while seeing denial as a step in our path rather than a roadblock. This perspective helped catalyze our progress towards acceptance. In doing so, we addressed the misconceptions and stigmas tied to our diagnosis. Now, we are prepared to move forward, equipped with these essential insights.

Part 2 examines the next stages of grief—sadness and anger.

Grief, like water, can be overpowering and intense. Yet, just as we moved through denial, we also have the strength to move through sadness and anger, ultimately finding our way toward healing.

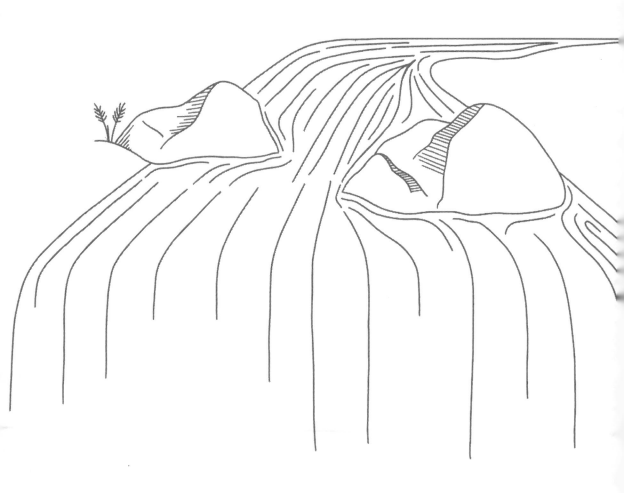

# PART 2

## Water—Sadness and Anger

*No one ever told me that grief felt so like fear.*
*C.J. Lewis*[5]

To write that moving through the stages of grief has been merely a whirlwind would be a profound understatement. For me, it has been an especially arduous journey, marked by a tumultuous roller coaster of emotions and life changing paradigm shifts in understanding myself. Sadness and anger were the lowest and most powerful emotional states for me.

I felt both fury and despair.

**I felt profound regret, not only for the difficulties that came with the diagnosis, but also for the years I had misunderstood myself.**

Anger raged through me—anger directed at myself and others for failing to recognize my problems earlier.

Only through feeling this heartache was I able to grow past it.

I can now see that the pain I experienced helped me plant a seed of hope in my soul.

Sadness deluged me like a furious downpour.

It was a difficult pill to swallow when I realized I might not be able to handle my ADHD on my own. It was like standing on the edge of a cliff, staring down into an infinite abyss, and knowing the only way forward was to plunge into the unknown. The realization that I needed medication to regulate my emotions was a hard reality that conveyed a sense of loss.

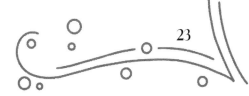

I was grieving for the person I thought I was and the life I thought I had.

I was overcome with sadness night after night. I cried myself to sleep, lamenting the loss of agency over my life. I felt marked and classified as someone in need of mental health services. The world moved on around me while I felt caught in my bubble of grief, left behind.

The sense of loss was palpable.

**Allow yourself a brief respite for introspection.**

**Is there a resemblance to your personal experience in these words?**

Within this whirlwind of sorrow, I found frustration growing in myself. Looking back at my teenage years, I should have known that other people my age were not having sex and using drugs. I don't know why I didn't realize I was different, that I couldn't do this on my own. Why couldn't I realize that it wasn't usual for a fourteen-year-old to go out drinking and wake up with their face flat on the pavement or in a strange house?

I don't know why I wasted my adolescent years being blind.

How could I not see that I needed help?

I now see that, during this period, I was gaslighting myself.

I repeatedly gave in to the concept that I was less-than-perfect because of some flaw in my character.

My rage was directed at my family—the very people I believed should have recognized the warning signs and helped me.

Why didn't they notice the signs?

Why didn't they step in?

Why did they allow my precious teenage years to fade into the background without stopping me from making poor decisions time and time again?

**I was drowning in regret.**

Every decision and every experience was scrutinized, wondering how different my life could have been if my ADHD had been identified earlier. "What-if" scenarios swirled around me like a tornado, igniting the fires of my rage. I was grieving the life I thought had been stolen from me, not simply the life I had.

**This rage was consuming.**

It gnawed at me, reminding me of the past, of missed possibilities. It was as if I had an open wound, and each thought of *what may have or what could have* been was like rubbing salt into that wound.

Nonetheless, as overwhelming as these emotions were, they were a necessary part of my road to acceptance. These were the harsh pills I had to swallow, the stumbling blocks I had to overcome. My rage served as a type of release, a means for me to express my grievances and come to grips with my history. The rage and despair I felt at this point held knowledge.

Wisdom, which I didn't realize I needed.

Wisdom hidden behind old pain.

Wisdom that needed to be seen.

**Wisdom that needed a voice.**

Despite the difficulties, every tear and moment of rage have been a step closer to acceptance, to a greater understanding of myself.

Sadness and anger, like water, can be peaceful or turbulent, reflective or overwhelming, life-sustaining or seemingly destructive. However, keep in mind that water is adaptive. It flows, forges new paths, and carves landscapes. Water returns to a condition of serenity.

We shall immerse ourselves in these waters at this stage of our journey, daring to explore the depths of our anguish and rage. Perhaps you feel sorrow washing over you like waves of despair. Perhaps you feel searing flashes of rage consuming you like a roaring storm.

I get it. Life is unfair.

The goal of this stage is not to ruminate on these emotions. Instead, give yourself permission to experience and understand them. **Your emotions are providing you data.** Data that is deep in wisdom. Data that needs to be heard. Let these emotions move through you, like a flowing stream. By engaging these feelings, we can begin to comprehend their origins and, eventually, learn how to navigate through them.

# Moving Forward

It's now your opportunity to explore these intense feelings. This is a time for contemplation and introspection, an opportunity to throw light on your own feelings of sadness and anger in the aftermath of your diagnosis.

The following thought-provoking prompts will help you interact with these emotions, investigate them fully, and recognize their impact on your life. You, like me, will go through the stages of sorrow—the depths of despair and the heights of rage.

This is not a process that can be rushed.

Take your time.

**Be gentle with yourself** and find comfort in the normalcy of experiencing emotions in your own way. Stay open to feeling, expressing, and exploring these sensations.

Allow these emotions to wash over you and pass through you. Remember that our emotions, like water, ebb and flow.

*Embrace the storm.*

Consider the weeks or months that followed your diagnosis. Our bodies are insightful teachers; they frequently show us how to process sorrow and grief in their own distinct ways.

Can you describe the physical feelings you felt when you learned of your diagnosis and how they affected you emotionally?

_____

_____

_____

_____

_____

Did you feel a deep sense of grief as if you had lost a part of yourself? How did this impact your day-to-day life and relationships?

_____

_____

_____

_____

_____

Alternatively, did you feel a burning sense of anger or frustration as if the world had been unfair to you?

_____

_____

_____

_____

_____

How did you cope with these emotions and channel them in a positive direction?

Or maybe you haven't yet coped with the diagnosis—that's okay.

Let the words fill these pages with whatever is bubbling up to the surface.

It's crucial to highlight that people may experience a complex mix of anger and sadness in the aftermath of a new diagnosis, and that these emotions aren't always simple to unravel or comprehend. **Grief is not a linear process, and it doesn't always make logical sense.**

If this is the case for you, fill in the blanks with details about your experience.

How did your despair and anger manifest in you at this time? How did it appear?

*Write a letter to your younger self.*

Express your disappointment regarding having not been diagnosed earlier.

Include vivid images that represent how you felt through those difficult times and, in addition, how you feel now as you reflect on that period of your life. As an example, here is the letter that I wrote to myself:

*Dearest Amy,*

*As I write this with a trembling hand, a gentle grief fills my heart for the wonderful childhood you deserved but didn't have.*

*Your childhood was a perpetual search for belonging—a quest for acceptance within cultural norms that allowed little opportunity for self-appreciation. Your desire for affection and approval from others overshadowed your desire for self-approval. This external validation, which seemed to be more important than your own view of yourself at times, came at the expense of your self-worth.*

*You were seduced by the fleeting attraction of a high school romance, enveloping your childhood in an enigma of unrequited love. It was a moment when you should have been fostering self-love. Instead, you let another's opinion possess you, depriving yourself of the valuable opportunity to understand and love your real self.*

*Your worth does not lessen because someone is unable to see it. Be kind to yourself. You are enough, just as you are.*

*There is one temptation, however, that you must reject with all your might. The temptation to escape reality via the cloud of substance addiction. Drugs and alcohol may give you a false sense of belonging and the confidence to stand out in a crowd, but they only conceal your wonderful self. Dimming your beautiful light.*

*Remember, in your finest form, you are lively and capable of connecting with people. True camaraderie cannot be discovered at the bottom of a bottle or in a cloud of smoke. It can be found in shared moments of laughter and meaningful conversations. It manifests itself in your ability to be present, to totally immerse oneself in the experience of life, free of any artificial veil.*

*Keep your head held high, young one. Accept your quirky nature and vivid personality. Take pleasure in your own company—it is in the solitude of self-acceptance that true self-love blooms. Know that you are deserving of every love you've desired, including your own. Be your strongest supporter, your greatest admirer, and keep an open heart.*

*May the wisdom in these words illuminate your way, and may you find strength in their truths as you continue on your road toward a life filled with self-love, healthy relationships, and unclouded joy. You are destined for a life that is far more meaningful than simply fitting in—a life of sublime belonging.*

Now friends, it's your turn. Use the space below to write your own letter:

_____

_____

_____

*Create a visual representation.*

Using the space below, draw a picture or create a collage that represents the emotions you're feeling during this stage. Use colors, shapes, and images to capture the intensity of your sadness and anger. Reflect on what these emotions mean to you.

*Participate in one or more of the following activities.*

Each activity has the potential to significantly enhance your experience. Although participating in just one exercise might provide significant benefits, there is no reason to limit yourself. Remember that the decision and the journey are all yours, allowing for a personalized exploration adapted to your own preferences.

**Toss pieces of paper with your negative ideas and emotions written on them into a blazing fire.** Watch them burn and turn to ash. With each piece of paper you throw in the fire, remember that you're releasing some of your misery and fury.

**Take a walk in the woods.** Notice the sights, sounds, and scents. Consider the feelings you're experiencing and how they're affecting you as you walk. Connect with the earth element and imagine it grounding you and assisting you in releasing some of your sadness and anger.

**Write a poem or song lyrics that express your feelings of despair and rage.** Use imagery and metaphors to express your emotions and the process of letting go. Consider how you might use this experience to grow and progress on your path to acceptance and self-love.

_____

_____

_____

_____

_____

*Try meditation.*

The road to recovery from the initial shock of a mental health diagnosis is not easy. It can be overwhelming and intensely emotional with bouts of melancholy, rage, perplexity, and despair. **I've certainly been there.**

However, from my personal experience, there are ways to find healing and calm in the midst of the storm. Meditation is, by far, the strongest tool I have. I've found clarity and acceptance by taking the time to stay with my emotions—to feel them fully and without judgment. In the resources section of this journal, you will find some of my favorite tools to use when you are ready to try guided meditations.

Before we move on, thank yourself for the work you've endured so far on this journey.

**You are brave.**

**You are strong.**

Part 3 dives into the depths of bargaining in which the ebb and flow of emotions intertwine with the gentle sway of the wind. We will navigate the intricate winds of negotiation and introspection, embrace the fluidity of our emotions, and seek solace in finding alternatives. Prepare to immerse yourself in this transformative phase. Allow the currents of reflection and resilience to carry you toward a renewed sense of self-discovery and understanding.

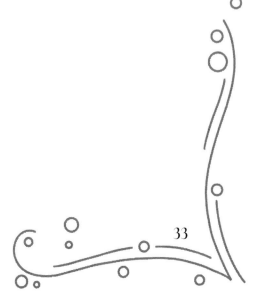

# PART 3

## Wind—Bargaining

*You think you know the shape of your life, how it's going to go, then you wake up one day and that shape changes. As much as you want to go back to that moment in time – that second before it changes – you can't.*
*Melody Beattie[6]*

Once I was able to adequately process my diagnosis of ADHD, I was catapulted into the eye of my own storm—a maelstrom of self-negotiation. Just as a hurricane begins with a gust of wind that grows into a ferocious storm, so did my attempts to deal with my diagnosis.

It started as wind whispers, queries that lightly rustled in my head: *If I could create the perfect routine, would I be able to skirt around the edges of this diagnosis? Could I strategize the use of my medication to control my need to take them daily?*

These whispers, however, suddenly turned into a howling gale, leading me to believe that I could barter my way out of the symptoms, using willpower as an umbrella against the impending downpour of my diagnosis.

This negotiating stage seemed like I was lost in a storm with little intervals of quiet in my mind that lulled me into a false sense of control, quickly followed by severe gusts of reality that forcefully reminded me of my predicament. The more I battled, the stronger the winds blew, **flinging me deeper into the storm of bargaining and further away from the shores of the truth.**

This time was a test of endurance; the gusts pulled at my resolve and drained my energy. I tried to outmaneuver the storm—to reach an agreement—but the storm of my diagnosis was unstoppable. Relentless.

Once the storm of my resistance ended and I surrendered to my reality, I witnessed a clearer world. A calmer world. A lightening.

In retrospect, the cyclone of bargaining was a manifestation of my urgent need to recover control over the stress caused by the diagnosis. It was a fruitless undertaking, like trying to direct a cyclone, a struggle against the inevitable. I was fighting the storm by rejecting the flow. I was depleting myself in the process.

It was during this turbulent period of negotiation that I gained insight, seeing the futility of my opposition. True resilience, I discovered, is found not in battling the storm, but in experiencing it.

Remember, the hurricanes of bargaining are a natural pause on the route toward acceptance. While it may appear intimidating and overwhelming, similar to a hurricane at sea, it will eventually subside. No storm lasts forever.

The tempest of negotiation, like a storm clearing the air for a brighter day, eventually leads to purifying skies and calmer waters. We'll learn to weather our storms at this stage, harnessing its strength to guide us toward acceptance, understanding, and healing.

As we turn our focus to the rising storm clouds on the horizon, it's time to brace ourselves for the voyage through this bargaining storm. We must fight the emotional volatility of this stage in the same way that a ship must face the towering seas and powerful winds of a storm at sea. However, keep in mind that storms, no matter how violent, are about more than only survival. They expose our latent strengths, resilience, and adaptability.

# Moving Forward

The goal here is to learn how to navigate the storm, not to command it. The following questions and exercises will serve as your compass and anchor, guiding and grounding you.

As you negotiate, haggle, and wrestle with your diagnosis, they will inspire introspection and give voice to your inner dialogue.

Through these exercises, you'll dive into your emotional storm, exploring your bargaining techniques and how they may have formed your connection with your diagnosis.

It's an invitation to enter your storm, learn from it, and emerge with a better awareness of your own abilities and qualities.

Remember, while preparing to enter the storm, the turbulence you will encounter is part of the journey toward acceptance.

On the other side, like the eye of the storm, serenity awaits.

The storm is not your enemy; it's a necessary path to sunlight and clear skies.

Bargaining is an important aspect of your journey through loss, an unavoidable storm that you are completely prepared to withstand.

**Hold on to your fortitude, let your emotions to rise and fall like the raging waves, and remember that the wind is carrying you to the peace that lies beyond.**

Prepare to delve into the core of your storm right now. It is your journey through the storm that shapes you, not the storm itself.

*View bargaining via the lens of the element of wind.*

Just as the wind can be unexpected and stormy, so can bargaining emotions, which frequently includes pessimism, impatience, and a desire to regain control.

During this period, it's usual to play out "what-if" scenarios in an attempt to bargain with our diagnosis in the hopes of regaining a sense of normalcy. Let's begin by noticing and working through these emotions.

Reflect on a time when you found yourself bargaining with your diagnosis.

In which kinds of "what-if" scenarios did you engage?

How did these emotions feel?

Describe the moment you realized you couldn't control or change your diagnosis.

---

---

---

---

---

Wind is unpredictable. How do you relate to the element of wind during this stage of grief?

Do you feel like your emotions are constantly shifting and changing?

Or do you feel more rooted?

---

---

---

---

---

During the stage of bargaining, it's common to experience feelings of desperation and a desire to regain control. In what ways have you found yourself grasping for control since receiving your diagnosis?

_____

_____

_____

_____

What strategies have been helpful in regaining a sense of balance and acceptance?

_____

_____

_____

_____

*Write a meaningful letter to a close loved one.*

Please, dear reader, pause for a moment before we move on to the next task to assess your progress thus far.

Just because our minds want to hurry through something doesn't mean we can. These pages could find you either prepared to move on to the next step in your journey or completely unprepared. Both are okay.

You are both. Both options are acceptable. I wish I could reach through these pages and give you the big hug you deserve right now as I type these words. But I just can't do that. I can only encourage you to proceed carefully and gently. As you compose this letter, you may find the initial draft to be harsh, even nasty.

That's fine. That's also okay.

As you pick up a pen and a sheet of paper, imagine yourself sitting at a rustic wooden desk, the soft glow of candlelight illuminating the area around you.

Allow the words to flow from your heart as you write a letter to a loved one about your path of getting diagnosed.

Allow your emotions to flood the page with each stroke of the pen, communicating the rawness of your experience, the challenges you've encountered, and the power that has emerged from inside. Share with your loved one the significant impact the diagnosis has had on your life, acknowledging the challenges it has brought while also recognizing the hidden gifts it contains.

Describe the times when you struggled and were frustrated. Describe the tangled thoughts and overwhelming emotions. Give a realistic picture of the hurdles you've overcome, the mental battles you've waged, and the strength it takes to face each day with unshakable determination.

Don't stop there. Allow the ink to build a story of optimism and perseverance. Share with your loved one the incredible abilities and unique perspectives that your neurodivergent mind provides to the world. Describe the moments of clarity, inventiveness, and deep empathy that have arisen during your journey, presenting a vivid portrayal of the gifts that lie within.

Finally, thank them for their unfailing love and support—for being a pillar of strength in your life. Invite them to celebrate the beauty and authenticity of your neurodivergent self with you, knowing that your mutual understanding and acceptance will form an unbreakable friendship.

Allow your thoughts and emotions to flow freely while you write this letter. When you're finished, seal it with love. Keep it as a strong reminder of your self-discovery and growth journey.

Although the option to share this letter is entirely yours, I strongly advise you to think about it. Your words have enormous power. Your story matters. By sharing your experience with a loved one, you not only strengthen your bond but also open the path for better understanding and acceptance.

As we complete this part on bargaining, keep in mind that this is only the beginning of your path to healing and flourishing. We are now preparing to enter the next stage of the grief process: flourishing.

# PART 4

## Earth—Flourishing

*The amazing thing about shifting from harsh criticism to kindness is that moments of difficulty – including situations that elicit feelings of shame and inadequacy – become an opportunity to both give and receive love.*
*Kristin Neff[7]*

Following my ADHD diagnosis, self-awareness dawned on me like a room slowly brightened by a dimmer switch, not with a sudden flash but a gradual illumination of my inner universe. This journey was similar to carefully wiping away layers of dust from a mirror, each stroke revealing more of the true reflection hidden amidst the hustle and overwhelming expectations of daily life. It was a process of rediscovery, gently uncovering the genuine self that had been obscured.

This realization was akin to unearthing a long-buried tome of forgotten tales about myself, every page intertwined with roots yearning for nourishment and sunlight. I delved into its chapters, immersing myself until the pulse of the words mirrored the rhythm of my heart, echoing with the ancient cadence of Earth herself.

In this profound reunion with my true essence, I felt layers of societal conditioning crumble away, much like how the earth generously receives fallen leaves, transforming them into nurturing soil.

It was a process of unbinding, a freeing from the choreographed steps the world had superimposed upon me. Now, in the sacred space of my own being,

45

I danced to the authentic rhythm of my soul—a melody that reverberates with the rich symphony of life that Earth herself orchestrates.

During this transformation, I discovered that I was not only developing. I was also flourishing. With each revelation of my quirks, weaknesses, and what some may call annoyances, I learned a way to use them as roots of empowerment. The hyperfocus that occasionally lost me in a sea of details became a beacon, guiding me to unrivaled depths of concentration. My once misunderstood overly sensitive nature blossomed into a nurturing soil rich with empathy, enabling me to connect with others and navigate the intricate depths of the human soul. My capacity to creatively and quickly handle difficulties was no longer an occasional trait but a consistent companion on my trip.

This stage of acceptance, like the fertile earth nurturing a seed into full bloom, went beyond simply accepting my diagnosis. It was about accepting the whole range of my humanity. The shadow and the light. It was about recognizing the power of my intellect, honoring its uniqueness, and maximizing its potential. It became a grounding journey into the very essence of who I am.

Flourishing is a journey beyond mere acceptance. It beckons us to shed societal conditions and to try on the layer of skin that is ours.

It forces us to pause.

It forces us to smile at ourselves.

It is through flourishing that we welcome the season of life and bow to our quirks seeing them as cherished treasures, not just tolerated oddities.

Flourishing is the rebirth of our entire, authentic selves from the ashes of our old selves. It is here that we find our strength because of our Unique Minds.

Now, my reader, having navigated the turbulent waters of denial, anger/sadness, and bargaining, I ask you to join me in the true joy of accepting the entire spectrum of your wonderful, unique self.

Acceptance and appreciation of our neurodivergent identities act as grounding forces, similar to the earth's gravitational pull, anchoring our souls in the unabashed expression of who we truly are. Take heart if you aren't yet anchored in this condition of self-acceptance. The path is gradual, but each step brings you closer to the goal of self-love and sincerity.

The act of revealing your truth, of removing the masks that disguise your unique neurodivergent identity, reverberates with transforming potential, just as a silent forest hums with a peaceful vibration. Speaking up and making a change in the world may be a significant act of self-honor and bravery.

# Moving Forward

As we journey through the process of flourishing, it is critical to recognize the camouflage we may have worn in our attempts to fit into the background of society's conventions. This is known as "masking". It demonstrates how we conceal our neurodivergent tendencies in order to avoid the pitfalls of social rejection.

Masking in neurodivergent people refers to a variety of tactics used to integrate into neurotypical culture. This could include people with autism, ADHD, anxiety, or other neurodivergent people suppressing their natural behaviors, interests, or feelings in order to portray a more "normal" picture.

In public places, for example, a person with autism may intentionally avoid their natural tendency to avoid eye contact, hum or rock out of fear of being judged or misunderstood. Similarly, a person with ADHD may try to hide evidence of distractibility or impulsivity to portray an image of attention and self-control.

I was quite skilled at masking. Constantly trying to fit in while fearing the moment when others might see through the façade. It was like living as an imposter, appearing successful yet feeling like a fraud. This was because my identity was lost to please others, a tactic to mask my anxiety, sense of overwhelm, and the persistence feeling that someday people would see that I am not good enough. That I am not worthy. That I have been pretending all along. That I had been faking at life.

**Masking is like an intensive, never-ending performance**. It necessitates constant monitoring and perpetual effort to preserve a veneer of neurotypicality. This act can be extremely tiring and unpleasant for neurodivergent people, taking them to the verge of burnout.

Long-term consequences of this performance can range from anxiety and sadness to a separation from one's genuine self, leaving individuals feeling lost in their own identity. Strangers to themselves. However, the path to acceptance and self-love requires us to discard these masks, stand tall in our unique neurodivergent identities, and reclaim the story of our own lives.

Further, once fully surrendered to the diagnosis, a neurodiverse person can learn when to mask as it suits them.

Masking can be reframed as a gift and shift from being disempowering to empowering.

# Moving Forward

Let's dig deeper into masking.

*1. Discover techniques to reduce masking and embrace the unique hues of your neurodivergent identities as strengths.*

Consider a recent memory, an encounter, or an event that required your participation.

Did you feel compelled to create a persona, to deliver prepared dialogues, to weave a performance that would secure acceptance and blend you in with the crowd?

_____

_____

_____

_____

_____

How did your mind, heart, and body react before, during, and after?

_____

_____

_____

_____

_____

_____

_____

_____

Probe into your memories for instances when you were forced to build a fortress around your true self, creating an impenetrable shell to protect your neurodivergent traits from the world.

What fueled this urge to mask?

How did it feel to bury a part of your identity beneath a pile of forced normality?

_____

_____

_____

_____

_____

_____

_____

In the vast spectrum of environments you traverse, some spaces let you drop your guard and embrace your authentic self.

What makes these spaces a sanctuary for your spirit?

How do they contrast with the landscapes where you're compelled to mask your neurodivergent tendencies?

---

Imagine a world stripped of stigmatization and negative perceptions around neurodivergent traits—a world where you're free to radiate your authentic self, with no compulsion to mask.

How would such a world reshape your life?

What transformations would you undergo? How would your interactions evolve?

Take a moment to deeply think about how masking can empower you at times.

For example, masking can serve as a coping strategy to set boundaries with friends or colleagues. It can serve as a powerful tool as you are thrown into new environments.

How might masking intentionally be used as an empowerment tool for you?

_____

_____

_____

_____

_____

## 2. Welcome a glimmer of hope.

Our neurodivergent identities blossom with distinct abilities that distinguish us. Recognizing and accepting our unique characteristics open the door to uncovering our talents, unraveling our potential, and thriving in a world that may not always understand our identity. So, it's time to take a moment to appreciate the gifts our neurodivergent minds bring to our lives.

You are a storehouse of uncommon talents, a mind that pushes beyond limitations and sees opportunities where others see barriers. There may have been times when your distinctive characteristics were suppressed or misunderstood, causing you to conceal your genuine essence. However, it is now time to show these distinguishing characteristics, demonstrating a natural ability to connect abstract ideas, understand diverse viewpoints, tune in to minor adjustments in your environment, and exhibit heightened sensitivity. These characteristics—your unique abilities—are the keys that can open doors leading to your goals, allowing you to navigate life in ways that go beyond the boundaries of conventional wisdom.

Now, we embark on an expedition within ourselves to unearth the gems that make us exceptional. Reflect on your inherent talents, your superior skills, and the experiences that sculpted your identity. Let the following prompts guide your introspection:

What activities ignite a spark in you? In other words, what can you do all day without once looking at the clock and checking the time?

Recall an accomplishment that seemed improbable to others. What strengths became your allies in achieving this milestone?

Describe the happiest times in your life. What were you doing then? How did your neurodivergent strengths infuse a sense of joy and fulfillment in these moments?

Imagine talking with a stranger. What facets of your personality would you wish to share? How can your unique talents make a positive impact on the world?

Reflect on the strengths that you've just noted. If you were to meet someone who possessed these strengths, what would you tell them? How would you support someone who had these strengths during a difficult time? What words would you use to encourage this person?

_____

_____

_____

_____

_____

_____

_____

_____

_____

Now, look back on the previous prompt and read it to yourself. Out loud. Often times, the words we tell ourselves (our inner dialogue) are words we would never use with others. It's time to start being a friend to yourself. This is a pivotal moment in your life; embrace the urgency of self-love.

Take a moment to process how these activities are resonating with you. We often don't take the time to celebrate our strengths the way we deserve. Thank you for showing up and doing that for yourself. Your neurodivergent strengths shape your identity, making you unique. Take pleasure in your distinct thinking and the abilities that make you who you are.

As we near the end of this journal, we will examine the final stage of processing, integration, via the lens of the element of space. This stage is a mash-up of reflection, integration, and connection, where we see how our experiences shape us and how we might channel them into a meaningful existence.

Let's enter the final part of our transformative journey.

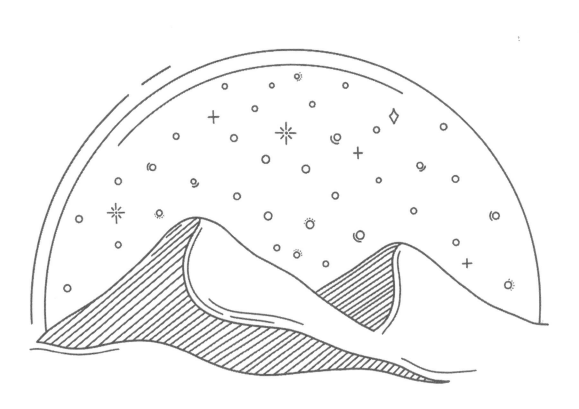

# PART 5

## Space—Integration

*Grief does not change you, Hazel. It reveals you.*
*John Green*[8]

As we approach the end of this guided journal, we find ourselves exploring the vast terrain of integration. My ADHD diagnosis was not a final chapter for me. Instead, it was an illuminating prologue to the unwritten chronicles of my life. Standing on a hilltop provides a panoramic view of the numerous components of our lives, illuminating the intricate connections that contribute to the magnificent landscape of our existence—the symphony of our minds and the natural world around us.

My path to integration began with the disclosure of my diagnosis. I revealed my ADHD diagnosis when I met new individuals and made new friends. There was no longer any need to conceal or disguise myself. I was revealing my true self including all the complexities and quirks. It was no longer about complying to cultural conventions or being afraid of being judged. It was about accepting and enjoying my individuality. Do you know what? A lot of people now share their stories with me in ways I suspect they would never have shared before. This is a gift.

I maintain the same candor and authenticity in professional contexts. My ADHD diagnosis is shared with potential employers. I express my requirements openly and boldly, requesting accommodations that will help me to thrive at work. This step is critical (not just for obtaining the necessary help) for breaking down the stigma associated with neurodivergence in professional settings.

Finding a community of other neurodivergent people was like discovering an oasis in the desert. Our common experiences formed a bond, a collective strength that energized us all. We celebrated our creativity, the superpowers bestowed upon us by our neurodivergent brains. These bonds highlighted the fact that our problems and successes were not isolated.

Recognizing and capitalizing on pattern recognition, a particular strength of neurodivergent thinking, has been an integral part of my integration path. Our brains thrive at linking disparate ideas and distilling complex challenges into simple concepts. This capacity frequently distinguishes us and occasionally draws misguided advice from neurotypicals such as "stay in your own lane" or demands for more context in our speech. However, it is our ability to recognize and connect dots across multiple thoughts and landscapes that defines us.

Integration goes beyond accepting and living with my diagnosis. It entails intentionally incorporating it into my worldview, utilizing it as a lens to better understand myself and the world around me. It's about recognizing the worth and potential of my neurodivergent thinking and channeling it into living a meaningful life. This stage has been exhilarating and empowering, teaching me how nature and our minds interconnect.

Cherish the distinct perspectives, creative sparks, and resilience that our neurodivergent identities bring into our lives. The path may be difficult at times, but the prospect of arriving at a state of integration—of harmony with our genuine selves—makes it worthwhile.

# Moving Forward

Now that we're on the verge of the last stage, I want to take a moment to reflect on the journey we've had together. Allow the teachings of acceptance, negotiation, and integration to act as guideposts for you. It's time to reflect on your individual path that you've taken within this journal. Every stride you've taken, every tear you've shed, and every moment of vulnerability have been a testament to your bravery and strength.

*Look back on your trip with fresh eyes.*

As you reflect on where you are in your journey of processing your diagnosis, remember that you have endured a lifetime of reflection and processing through an awakened mind. What will you do with it? How will you integrate your new self into your future self?

How will you look at the world?

How will you show up for others?

_____

_____

_____

_____

_____

How will you express yourself in ways that are authentic and true to your neurodivergent identity?

_____

_____

_____

_____

_____

*Investigate how your unique thinking has influenced your life.*

What lessons have you taken away from your self-discovery journey? How have these teachings affected the person you are today?

63

Picture yourself staring up at the sharp peaks and ridges of a tall mountain. As you admire the scenery, think of the challenges you've faced and overcome on the path to self-acceptance and love. How did you use your strengths to triumph against adversity? How can you put those same strengths to use to ensure your continued success?

Close your eyes and visualize yourself seated in a thick, green forest with towering trees and chirping birds. As you breathe in the fresh air and soak in the natural beauty around you, consider the ways in which you've connected with nature over the course of your journey. What lessons have you learned from the natural world? How have these lessons influenced your personal growth and development?

After reflecting on the lessons learned from nature in the serene setting of a lush forest, transition your thoughts to a different scene. Visualize yourself now standing in the midst of a powerful storm. In this moment, ponder how the tools and resources you've developed, inspired by nature's teachings, have equipped you to face life's turbulent times. How have these tools helped you navigate through the storms?

Integration calls for introspective maturity and the willingness to embrace every facet of one's identity, especially those that have been marginalized in the past. We can make the world a better place for ourselves and others by fully incorporating our experiences and neurodivergent identities into our sense of self. So, think about where you've been, where you're going, and how you can use your unique set of skills and experiences to make a positive difference in the world.

Dear reader,

Strength is loud. Streng[th is quiet.]
Strength is believing. Str[ength is]
Strength is trying.
Strength is failing.
Strength is showin[g]
Strength is boundaries.
Strength is accepting others. Stre[ngth is]
being loved. Strength is loving myself

You are strong and you are loved

xx

# CREATING MEANING THROUGH YOUR DIAGNOSIS

*The world breaks everyone and afterward many*
*are strong at the broken places.*
*Ernest Hemingway[9]*

Creating this guided journal and inviting you into my story has been my personal road to clarity. While a new diagnosis may make you feel overwhelmed or suffocated, remember that there is always a way forward. Accept your diagnosis and give yourself permission to experience the emotional spectrum that comes with it. You are paving the way for transformation. It's time to free your gifts and share them with the world. As we progress, we'll discover deeper layers of meaning and significance in your diagnosis.

# Moving Forward

We're about to embark on a huge introspection exercise: writing letters to our future selves.

We are moving away from the echoes of the past and toward the horizons of the future. This stage encourages you to examine your future self, and how your diagnosis might act as a catalyst for growth and transformation. Your thoughts, aspirations, and visions are welcome on the following pages. Consider who you want to be in five, ten, or twenty years from now. Think about how your diagnosis will shape the person you want to grow into.

Writing a letter to your future self can be a liberating experience. Outline your future goals and illuminate the lessons you've learnt along the way. Consider your journey of self-discovery and acceptance, and how it has shaped you. This is your chance to lay the foundation for the future you envision for yourself.

_____

_____

_____

_____

_____

_____

_____

_____

_____

_____

_____

As you conclude your letter to your future self, take a moment to seal it with a sense of hope and anticipation. Put this letter in an envelope as a sign of releasing the future and relinquishing control over it.  When you choose to open it in the future – be it in five, ten, or twenty years – may it serve as a profound reminder of your journey, your growth, and the seeds you have planted. Let this letter be a testament to the resilience and wisdom you've gained, a bridge connecting your present self to the person you want to be in the future. Remember that every word you write now has the potential to guide the person you will become tomorrow.

*Acknowledge your personal growth and evolution. Celebrate the unique qualities and treasures that make you, you.*

Appreciate the intricate, diverse adventure you've courageously undertaken. You've bravely explored the subtle dance of loss, intertwined with natural elements, and negotiated the maze of emotions that accompany a new mental health diagnosis. This has been a difficult but transformative trip. It's been an adventure that has most certainly changed your perspective on yourself and the world around you.

Allow this journal to rest and sit for a while (ideally for a thoughtful period of thirty days) to represent the rest and contemplation that you, too, require to absorb and process what you've learned and felt. This is an integration period—a sacred pause that allows your experiences to settle and germinate within your consciousness.

Consider your evolution when you return to these pages, armed with new insights and a better knowledge of your journey. Have you moved on from the initial tumultuous storm of diagnosis? Have you started to notice the brilliant, ever-changing hues of your remarkable divergent thinking, recognizing the distinct strength each shade represents? Or have you found yourself skirting, tiptoeing around the tangled web of emotions triggered by your diagnosis?

Examine the person you've become since starting this journal. Have you observed any changes in your attitude toward your diagnosis? Are there any specific moments of revelation, breakthrough, or transformation that stand out?

_____

_____

_____

_____

_____

_____

_____

Consider the severe challenges you've faced since your diagnosis. What tactics have you used to deal with them? Were there any strategies that were effective or transformative?

_____

_____

_____

_____

_____

_____

_____

_____

_____

Dive into your identity's domain of distinct strengths. How have you used your unique gifts and unusual wisdom to ignite positive change in your life or the world around you?

_____

_____

_____

_____

_____

_____

_____

Are there locations where you feel stuck or suffocated? How can you approach these difficulties with increased compassion and self-awareness?

_____

_____

_____

_____

_____

_____

_____

This voyage, like the rhythm of life itself, does not follow a straight path. There are detours, dangers, and rest stops. When the route becomes steep or the load feels too heavy, it's natural to pause or retreat.

When you return to this journal, you will have a new perspective and renewed enthusiasm. This will allow you to continue your journey toward acceptance, integration, and self-love. You are becoming an expert navigator of your own experience, learning to trust your instincts and increasing in your ability to support yourself in important, healing ways as you go through this process.

Let the knowledge you've gathered on this journey guide you ahead. Accept your newfound understanding of your unique mind and contemplate how it might color your future. Above all, remember to be gentle with yourself as you continue along this road. You're not just surviving; you're thriving. You're learning to thrive in your magnificent neurodivergent world every day.

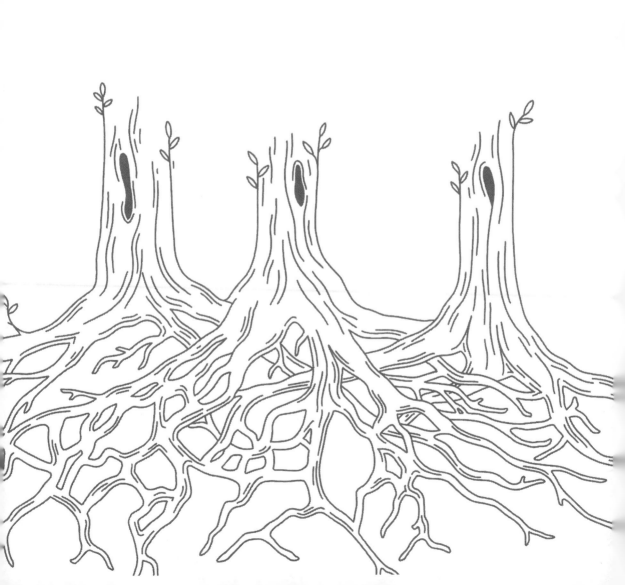

# CONCLUSION

## Resilience Through Community

*Deep grief sometimes is almost like a specific location, a coordinate on a map of time. When you are standing in that forest of sorrow, you cannot imagine that you could ever find your way to a better place. But if someone can assure you that they themselves have stood in that same place, and now have moved on, sometimes this will bring hope.*
*Elizabeth Gilbert*[10]

When I was first diagnosed with ADHD, I felt an intense need to hide and control my symptoms. I was all set to put on a front, to conceal my genuine identity. I didn't feel safe to reveal my true self. But when I started to be more open and honest about my life, I saw that I wasn't the only one going through this.

There were lots of others, like me, who are trying to make sense of a new and late diagnosis of ADHD. This insight drove me to investigate the huge online realm of social media in search of like-minded individuals with whom I might bond over our common experiences.

Online support groups encouraged me to start talking about my ADHD experiences. To better comprehend other people's points of view, I found myself empathizing with their stories, sharing wisdom gained from my own experience, and asking curious questions.

I feel a growing sense of peace and oneness as I spend more time in this welcoming online group. **Knowing that other people are experiencing something similar is comforting.** It assures me (and, I hope, others) that we are never alone on our journeys no matter how difficult they may be.

A single step can pave the way for an incredible adventure. You may be shocked to discover how far you've come as you reflect on the twisting path you've traveled since you first started this journal. Your internal fortitude has been crucial to your success on this journey. This resilience was created in the fires of honest self-examination, unconditional love, and acceptance. We're getting closer to the end of our collective journey, so it's a good moment to shine a light on an underappreciated source of fortitude—the strength of community.

The essence of resilience is not just survival, but also growth, the ability to recover from adversity stronger and wiser. Personal fortitude is essential for resilience. However, resilience is not a solitary path. It grows in groups that understand and empathize with our journey. This strength is found in the hearts and minds of a community that shares our experiences and empathizes with our journey.

**As neurodivergent people, we often have an intrinsic ability to delve deeply into the emotional intricacies of ourselves and others, empathizing with a depth unknown to many.** This is a strength, a superpower, that we can use to build our communities by offering and accepting help.

A neurodivergent community is more than just a group of people who have the same condition. Through our community, we create a safe haven where we can find peace, support, and learn from people who also have unique minds.

A community's strength, however, is not a monologue. It lives on reciprocity, on the giving and receiving of help, empathy, and understanding. By reaching out to others and sharing our experiences and thoughts, we not only enhance our community but further our own journey of self-acceptance and understanding.

Consider a tree in a forest. Under the weight of a storm, it can swing and even fall on its own. However, in a forest, with roots entwined and branches reaching out to one other, they can withstand even the most violent storms.

We, too, are like trees in a forest, with our lives intertwined, our experiences shared, and our resilience strengthened by one another.

**Take a breather here. How does this relate to your own experience?**

Reaching out to others, especially those who are just starting out on their neurodivergent path, can have a huge influence. It's like reaching out a hand to someone who is lost in a labyrinth to show them that they are not alone and that there is a route out through the meandering paths. Your journey, your experiences, and your thoughts can serve as a guiding light for others while also enhancing your own understanding and resilience.

A vibrant, compassionate, and supportive neurodivergent group has the capacity to influence neurodivergence narratives in the broader cultural context. We can confront misunderstandings, tear down stigmas, and campaign for the acceptance and inclusion of neurodivergent individuals in all aspects of life when we band together, share our stories, and give our voices to the conversation.

Furthermore, as we assist others in navigating their path, we indirectly assist ourselves. We learn new views by sharing our experiences, and we gain strength by helping. This mutual process creates a positive feedback loop, which strengthens our resilience and deepens our sense of belonging.

As we approach the conclusion of this introspective journey, I encourage you to forge a bond with the neurodivergent community. This book was born not from a desire for accolades, but from a heartfelt need I felt upon my own diagnosis—a resource that was absent until now. My driving purpose has been to reach out and assist those walking a path similar to mine. Now, I invite you to reflect on how you might extend that same hand of support to others.

In the space below, contemplate how you can harness the insights you've gained to make a difference. Will you guide someone navigating the maze of diagnosis? Or perhaps share insights about the stages of grief with someone in your circle? As you move forward with newfound understanding, ponder the ways you can contribute to a community that thrives on mutual support.

When cultivating a community of support and strength, remember to extend to others the same understanding, empathy, and compassion that you have for yourself. Recognize their hardships without passing judgment, honor their path, and enjoy their triumphs as if they were your own.

# AFTERWORD

*And once the storm is over, you won't remember how you made it through, how you managed to survive. You won't even be sure, whether the storm is really over. But one thing is certain. When you come out of the storm, you won't be the same person who walked in. That's what the storm's all about.*

*Haruki Murakami*[11]

**M**y biggest hope is that embarking on this introspective journey has **reshaped you.** From initial shock to the serene plains of self-love, you've traversed emotional landscapes most can't imagine. Admire the distance you've covered and the strength you've shown.

Your journey reflects the rings of a tree—each layer unique, telling its own story. Through fires of denial and waters of doubt, you've found your grounding, you've rebuilt your roots.

But remember, this is not an end. It's a beginning. Your experience stands as a testament to your resilience and growth—a beacon reminding you of lessons learned and stories told.

You've transformed, not merely by confronting challenges, but by embracing them. Through life's storms, you've flourished, grounding yourself in the richness of your neurodivergence.

**Your unique neurological makeup is not a limitation; it's a testament to the multifaceted beauty of the human mind.** Celebrate this milestone as the start of an authentic life—a life where you don't just endure but thrive.

Thank you for embarking on this journey, showcasing the power of the human spirit. Your commitment to celebrating neurodiversity adds much needed vibrance and texture to our shared world. Remember, the path is continuous, winding, and enriched by shared experiences.

I'm deeply grateful for your courage and dedication. Together, we're pioneering a movement of acceptance, highlighting the exceptional talents within neurodivergence. I wish you boundless joy on your continued path. May you be filled with righteous self-love. Shine brightly as your adventure continues to unfold.

Here's to your journey. Here's to the chapters yet to be written.

# PERSONAL THOUGHTS

# GLOSSARY

**ADHD**: A neurodevelopmental condition characterized by inattention and hyperactivity-impulsivity.

**Advocacy**: Publicly supporting neurodivergent rights.

**Coping mechanisms**: The ways people handle stress.

**Empathy**: Understanding and feeling another's emotions.

**Integration**: Integrating one's neurodivergent identity into their self-perception and life.

**Introspection**: Engagement of deep self-reflection.

**Journey**: Self-discovery, acceptance, and knowledge of neurodivergence in this journal.

**Masking**: Hiding one's genuine self to fit in.

**Neurodivergent**: People with neurological disorders like ADHD, autism, dyslexia, and more. Someone who processes information differently.

**Neurotypical**: People with typical neurological development and functioning.

**Processing**: Mental functions used to interpret, categorize, and make sense of information, especially in comprehending and accepting neurodivergence.

**Resilience**: Quickly recovering from setbacks.

**Self-acceptance**: Accepting one's strengths and weaknesses without judgment.

**Societal conditioning**: Norms, values, beliefs, and expectations imposed by society that shape our behavior and thinking.

**Self-discovery**: Learning about oneself via life experiences and reflection.

**Self-love**: Embracing the flaws of your humanity in a way that generates kindness and compassion.

# NOTES

**Title Page**

    1. **Keep some room**: Mary Oliver, *Evidence: Poems*, (2009), 57.

**Foreword**

    2. **Males are more likely to:** Nancy L. Nussbaum, *ADHD and Female Specific Concerns: A Review of the Literature and Clinical Impressions.* Journal of Attention Disorders, 16 no. 2 (2012).

    3. **Undiagnosed females often:** Darby. E. Attoe and Emma *A. Miss-Diagnosis: A Systematic Review of ADHD in Adult Women.* Journal of Attention Disorders, 27 no. 7 (2023).

**Part I**

    4. **I am holding:** Tallu Schuyler Quinn. *What we Wish Were True: Reflections on Nurturing Like and Facing Death*, (2022), 207.

**Part II**

    5. **No one ever:** C.J. Lewis, *A Grief Observed*, (2015), 21.

**Part III**

    6. **You think you know:** Melody Beattie, *The Grief Club: The Secret to Getting Through All Kinds of Change*, (2006), 307.

**Part IV**

    7. **The amazing thing:** Kristen Neff, *Fierce Self Compassion: How Women*

*Can Harness Kindness to Speak up, Claim Their Power, and Thrive*, (2021), 116.

Part V

    8. **Grief does not:** John Green, *The Fault in Our Stars*, (2014), 297.

Creating Meaning

    9. **The world breaks:** Ernest Hemingway, *A Farewell to Arms*, (1957), 316.

Conclusion

    10. **Deep grief sometimes:** Elizabeth Gilbert, *Eat, Pray, Love: One Women's Search for Everything Across Italy, India, and Indonesia*, (2007), 174.

Afterword

    11. **And once the:** Haruki Murakami, *Kakfa of the Shore*, (2002), 11.

# ADDITIONAL RESOURCES

## Books

Brewer, Judson. *Unwinding Anxiety: New Science Shows How to Break the Cycles of Worry and Fear to Heal Your Mind*. New York: Avery Publishing, 2022.

Hari, Johann. *Stolen Focus: Why You Can't Pay Attention and How to Think Deeply Again*. New York: Crown Publishing Group, 2022.

Nerenberg, Jenara. *Divergent Mind: Thriving in a World that Wasn't Designed for You*. California: HarperOne, 2021.

Pink, Richard, and Roxanne Emery. *Dirty Laundry: Why Adults with ADHD are so Ashamed and What we Can Do to Help*. California: Ten Speed Press, 2023.

Rosier, Tamara. *Your Brain is Not Broken: Strategies for Navigating Your Emotions and Life with ADHD*. Michigan: REVELL, 2021.

Solden, Sari. Women with Attention Deficit Disorder, 2nd Edition. Michigan: Introspect Press, 2012.

## Articles

ADDitude editors. "Why ADHD in Women is Routinely Dismissed, Misdiagnosed, and Treated inadequately. *ADDitude Magazine*, January 13, 2021.

Connolly, Maureen. "ADHD in Girls: The Symptoms That Are Ignored in Females." *ADDitude Magazine*, October 2, 2019.

Saline, Sharon S. "Q: The Social Strain of ADHD Weighs Heavy on My Daughter." *ADDitude Magazine*, July 12, 2023.

# Podcasts

Brooks, Mel. "Conquer Overwhelm: Your Ultimate Guide to Inner Peace With Amazing Dr. Thema Bryant." *The Mel Brooks Podcast*. October 11, 2023.

Brooks, Mel. "If You Only Listen to One Podcast Today, Make it This One." *The Mel Brooks Podcast*. September 3, 2023.

Cannon, Donae. "Your Brain's Not Broken: Convergent Vs. Divergent Thinking (Interview with Dr. Tamara Rosier)." *ADHD Crash Course*. June 20, 2023.

McGillicuddy, Tara and Edris, Lynne. "Resources: Managing ADHD Storms (Interview with James Ochoa)." *ADHD Support Talk Radio*, July 18, 2023.

Otsuka, Tracy. Amy Jo "The Difficulty of Diagnosing ADHD in Women and Girls with Dr. Grace Esan." *ADHD for Smart Ass Women*, April 27, 2022.

Otsuka, Tracy. "How to Live to Your Potential with ADHD." *ADHD for Smart Ass Women*, March 3, 2021.

Otsuka, Tracy. "Women with ADHD Medication with Dr. Carolyn Lentzsch-Parcells." *ADHD for Smart Ass Women*, May 5, 2021.

Rogers, Rozanne. Chats in the Attic- An ADHD Audio Series. *ADHD: Let's Talk*. October 2023.

# Websites

Attention Deficit Disorder Association. "The Attention Deficit Disorder Association." Last accessed October 17, 2023. https://www.add.org.

ADDitude. "ADDitude: Trusted Resource for Families and Adults with ADHD and Related Conditions." Last accessed September 15, 2023. https://www.additudemag.com/.

CHADD. "Psycho-Education Regarding the Nature of ADHD: CHADD (Children and Adults with Attention Deficit Disorder)." Last accessed October 17, 2023. https://www.chadd.org.

# ACKNOWLEDGMENTS

To my wonderful husband Kevin and cherished daughter Avy, you have my deepest appreciation. Throughout the entire journey of writing this journal, you both have been unwavering in your support and encouragement. Kevin, your patience and unflinching loyalty, both during the times of my undiagnosed and later-diagnosed ADHD, have been nothing short of extraordinary. Your patience, kindness, and love have been my anchors. For that, I am profoundly grateful. Your unconditional affection inspired me to embrace my neurodiversity and share my story with the world. And to my dearest Avy, I am thrilled to assure you that you will play the role of illustrator in mommy's next book adventure.

I also want to thank Natalie Lemos. In one of my darkest hours, Natalie was more than just a friend; with her unwavering support, she showed up for me when I needed it the most. This truly sets her apart as nothing less than a Unicorn Mom.

I would also like to extend my heartfelt thanks to Jaima Zollinger. She is more than just the illustrator of this journal; she is a cherished friend. Jaima is someone I deeply admire and continually learn from. Without her, this journal would simply not be what it is today. Thank you, dearest Jaima, for everything.

I also wish to express my heartfelt appreciation to Lena Berry. Lena, as a beta reader, your insights and feedback were invaluable, but it was your ability to connect with the essence of my work that left an indelible mark on my heart. Thank you for being part of this journey and for understanding my vision in a way that I will never forget.

I'd like to extend my gratitude to the brave people who have confided in me and allowed me to learn from their experiences—both the good and the bad. These accounts, both personal and anecdotal, have been beacons on dark evenings, helping me feel less alone and more a part of a dynamic community of folks facing similar challenges. Let's keep lighting each other's way as we make our way through the winding roads of neurodiversity and introspection.

Every person who had any kind of hand in this project, however small, deserves a standing ovation.

This journal is the culmination of efforts by an incredible team of strong, fierce, and talented women. Jaima Zollinger, as previously mentioned, is a skilled illustrator whose talent brought my words and ideas to life. I am also deeply grateful to my editor, Celina Mina, for her invaluable assistance in organizing my scattered thoughts. To Holly Dunn, my cover and interior designer, for her expert guidance. And to Dr. Amy Yillik, for her remarkably written foreword.

This group of inspiring and tenacious women has been instrumental in helping me to realize what's possible when one challenges limiting beliefs. Each member of this team has played a pivotal role in supporting me through the arduous and often daunting task of self-publishing—a journey made even more challenging as a woman with ADHD. Their collective support and expertise have been invaluable in navigating the ups and downs of this complex process, empowering me to bring my vision to life despite the hurdles.

Finally, I'd like to say thanks to you, the reader, for coming along for the ride. Your courage, curiosity, and commitment to self-discovery, along with your pursuit of personal development, are evidence of the strength of the human spirit. Continue to learn about and appreciate the wonderful complexities of your neurodivergent nature.

# ABOUT THE AUTHOR

A profound and unexpected shift in her life set Amy Joynt on a new path. She bravely confronted her own mental health, an experience that not only transformed her life but also uncovered a critical need: empowering women who face a late ADHD diagnosis. Driven by passion, Amy is committed to creating and amplifying inclusive spaces where every neurodivergent individual is not just embraced but liberated—a place where they find their voice and use it.

Amy lives in Washington state with her husband and daughter. Professionally, she thrives as a school psychologist and takes joy in coaching women newly diagnosed with ADHD through Joynt Coaching and Consulting, her recently launched business. Outside of work, she cherishes expressing her creativity and building relationships with other neurodivergent women. Amy's dedication is unwavering. She champions those navigating the complexities of a new ADHD diagnosis, guiding them toward self-love, self-compassion, and peace, encouraging their badassery.

Made in United States
Troutdale, OR
02/12/2024

17630604R00071